Bimini

Tales of an Island Getaway

"Looking for Atlantis" previously appeared in *Body Mind Spirit* magazine.

Designed by Lissa Monroe
Cover photo taken from *Bimini by the Sea*

River City Publishing
1719 Mulberry St.
Montgomery, AL 36106

First Edition—2003
Printed in the United States of America
1 3 5 7 9 10 8 6 4 2

Library of Congress Cataloging-in-Publication Data:
Warner, David T., 1948-
Bimini : tales of an island getaway / David T. Warner.-- 1st ed.
p. cm.
ISBN 1-57966-046-0
1. Bimini Islands (Bahamas)--Description and travel. 2. Bimini
Islands (Bahamas)--Social life and customs. 3. Bimini Islands
(Bahamas)--Social conditions. 4. Bimini Islands (Bahamas)--Biography.
5. Warner, David T., 1948---Travel--Bimini Islands (Bahamas) I. Title.

F1659.B55 W37 2003
917.2'9604--dc22
2003019115

Bimini

Tales of an Island Getaway

David T. Warner

River City Publishing
Montgomery, Alabama

For Ossie

Everybody knows
A little place like Kokomo
Now if you wanna go
And get away from it all
Go down to Kokomo.

—Beach Boys, "Kokomo"

❧

"Soon after you saw the dark blur of Casuarina trees above the lines of the sea, you could see the white bulk of the house. Then, as you came close, you raise the whole length of the island with the coconut palms, the clapboarded houses, the white line of the beach, and the green of the South Island stretching beyond it."

—Ernest Hemingway, *Islands in the Stream*

❧

"I was in Bimini once, at a bar, and they said Hemingway got drunk right there and shot sharks from the dock with a machine gun and managed to hit himself in both legs."

—Dave Barry, *For the Love of Books*

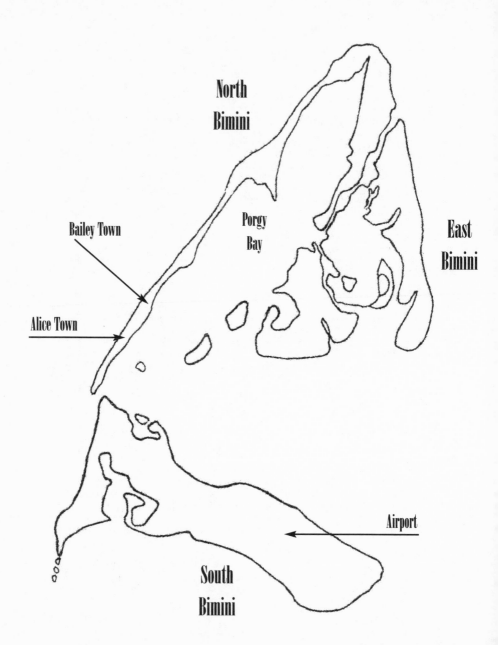

North
Bimini

Porgy
Bay

Bailey Town

Alice Town

East
Bimini

Airport

South
Bimini

Table of Contents

Devil

≈

Devil arrived every morning around nine to open the Compleat Angler Hotel and Bar for business. The two maids were waiting for him in the hardwood, rum-barreled lobby, and they started the morning with coffee and gossip. The night before, a drunken blonde from Oklahoma had removed her bikini panties and tacked them on the ceiling while dancing on the bar, and Devil's first chore was to throw them in the trash.

The End of the World Saloon, at the southern tip of the island, not the Angler, was the spot for such carryings-on, thought Devil.

Sweeping done, Devil flipped on the tape deck behind the bar. Eardrum-shattering island music blasted forth:

Devil "holding court" at the bar in the Compleat Angler

Never get a licking till you go down in Bimini.

Never get a licking till you go down in Bimini.

The first customer was Cap'n Dan. He'd been making the forty-eight-mile run to Bimini from Lauderdale on his thirty-four-foot Hatteras, the *Lucky Lady*, for over thirty years, and a 10 A.M. rum and Coke was nothing new to him.

Close on his heels was a middle-aged couple from Indianapolis. They'd flown in on a Chalk's seaplane out of Miami and walked, with Accident pushing a wobbly, four-wheeled cart loaded with their luggage, the quarter of a mile or so down the cracked and sandy, trash-strewn blacktop past mangy dogs, screaming Biminites, rusted machinery, and crumbling, partially finished concrete buildings and piers. A morning libation was unusual for them. But after that sordid preview of things to come, they needed one.

No sooner had the couple started in on their goombay smashes than a drug deal gone sour erupted in a noisy altercation on the outside patio. Hoisting his billy, Devil

Queen's Highway in Bimini

stepped outside to break it up. But the guilty parties had vanished amid a flurry of impotent curses.

It's going to be one of those days, thought Devil, his elfin face creasing in a grin.

*   ﹡

Aside from a room key lost on the beach—Devil threatened to charge the guest $100 to replace it, and it was miraculously recovered following some frantic digging in the sand—things ran smoothly until six.

Chalk's seaplane landing at Alice Town

Gary Hart

Devil was tallying up the day's receipts and getting ready to hand over the register to the nighttime bartender when Ossie, the owner-manager, arrived with a vaguely familiar-looking white man and his attractive blonde companion.

"Devil, meet Gary and Donna," said Ossie.

Following handshakes all around, Ossie bought the couple a round of Bahama mamas, topped with 151-proof rum, and began regaling them with island tales. Many

Bahama mamas later, the couple joined the Calypsonians on stage with Donna singing and Gary feebly shaking the maracas, a sickly grin on his face. When the band took a break, Donna asked Devil to snap a picture of them on stage with her 35mm Nikon, and the rest is history!

*

A week or so later, a *New York Times* reporter flew over to Bimini to research the story and asked Devil about his part in the passion play.

"Did you have any idea Gary Hart was running for president when you snapped his picture?" asked the reporter over a Chivas on the rocks.

Devil grinned his wicked grin. "I might've seen him on TV a time or two, but all you 'seaweeds' look alike to me."

Bimini
Islands
1982

≈

We'll get there fast
And then we'll take it slow.
Beach Boys, "Kokomo"

I'm strolling down the Queen's Highway in Bailey Town, past the colorfully dilapidated shacks, bars, churches, the Elks Home, and the YMCA that resembles a chartreuse bomb shelter when I spot Coconut, conveyor of luggage. "What you doing in Nigger Town, mon?"

Coconut resembles a Mack truck, with trouser cuffs hanging halfway up his calves, an insane, shit-eating grin, and ham hocks for hands. He can lift a grand piano on his shoulders and carry it across the Queen's Highway.

I'm on Bimini, once again. . . . The first time was ten years ago, and I drank in places like The End of the World Saloon, where disbarred (for alleged misuse of public funds) Harlem congressman, Adam Clayton Powell, hung out, and Opal's, run by a sad-faced brown lady who is everyone's adopted mother, especially Coconut's. I ended up smoking dope upstairs at the Compleat Angler with the proprietor, Ossie, and peered out the window at the harbor in the moonlight. The stars were like the fists of God.

I walked on the snow-white beach where the lights of Miami, fifty miles to the west, glimmered like the aurora borealis. I was in love with the island, and the natives were happy-go-lucky characters who could do no wrong. The air was soft like velvet, and the Atlantic was the clear color of dreams, with a milky consistency like damp cotton.

Later, I would find out differently about the natives, and there were many lessons the island would teach me, some not exactly pleasant, but all useful. The charm and

Manny Rolle, Hemingway's "Chair Boy" on the *Pilar* in the '30s

curse of Bimini is that it never changes. Your moods color it the color of the inside of your head. One minute, it's heaven—the next, hell.

On one trip over, I befriended a gay Anglican priest from Atlanta who had an unsentimental, though charitable, view of the natives. He saw them as epic fornicators and lechers with an aversion to family life, completely selfish with no ambition beyond the pursuit of pleasure for pleasure's sake but also generous and with a good outlook on life because they weren't hung up on material things as long as women and drink were available. They were beyond violence in a pacifistic never-never land, willing to let anyone do what he wants as long as it doesn't interfere with anyone else.

Another time, I met a drama professor from Northwestern. He was seventy-five years old and claimed to have had an affair with movie star Tyrone Power in the '30s, and Ty had been the love of his life. I knew what was coming and told him I was only intellectually interested in such things. He took me to dinner anyway and throughout the meal carried on a monologue about Shakespeare's having been gay. All the women in his plays were portrayed by men, and everyone, especially a would-be writer, should experience everything once. I told him he was too old to be flirting so shamelessly, and eventually he got the sad message.

I found myself drawn to the island like a magnet and visited often. I knew most of the natives by name and learned how their names reflected their characters. Dirty Red was a gambler, and Accident was always stumbling through life. The first time I met Accident, Ossie said, "Here comes trouble!" When he sat down at our table, his chair toppled over backward, and he reached for the table. Instead, he grabbed the tablecloth, and our drinks went everywhere!

"Acci" is like the tin woodsman, with steel rods in his arms and legs where they've patched him back together over the years, and he'll tell you about it with a glow of pride. Once he was in a car accident in Freeport. The three others in the car were killed instantly, but he was unscathed and probably will live to be a hundred and die in bed.

Another time, Acci took an elderly Midwestern couple bottom fishing off Bimini with his mate, Useless. The engine conked out in the Gulf Stream, and Acci and Useless abandoned ship and swam half a mile to the Turtle Rocks, leaving the panicked couple to their fate. Two days later, the couple was picked up by the Coast Guard, badly dehydrated and close to death.

One of the hellish experiences concerned Pam from Lauderdale, who was shaped like a Vogue model. She was something of a nymphomaniac and lived with a fifty-ish gangster named José. They were on a sixty-foot Chris-Craft, and I went drinking with them. Pam and José had an argument, and Pam asked me to dance. We started kissing, and José left. We went to my room at

Yama Bahamas, a whorehouse owned by Yama, a former contender for World Middle Weight Champ, and did the deed. Then Pam sent me downstairs for a drink. The natives in the bar applauded me as I came down the staircase, and I was deathly afraid José would find out.

Later Pam insisted I take her back to José's room. So I did but only knocked on the door and slipped off, leaving Pam alone after she fell drunkenly to the floor.

The next morning I ran into Pam on the street, and she told me that José had a gun and was looking for me. I spent the rest of the day dodging Pam and José. It seemed like everywhere I went, they followed. I wasn't sure Pam hadn't made the whole thing up. No piece of ass was worth this kind of aggravation!

The next day, I left.

*

This trip, I encounter the incredible Marty at the Compleat Angler. We have a few drinks and go out on the beach to smoke a joint with his henchman, Andy. Out at sea a spotlight combs the shore, and Marty figures it's his friend's boat that was to transport a big load of dope back to Lauderdale. The boat draws dangerously close till it's no more than fifty feet offshore, close to beaching if it heads south. Marty and Andy wave and scream like madmen, but the boat heads south toward shoal water and eventually goes out of sight. So Marty runs off to get his motor scooter.

The next morning, I discover Marty had saved the boat from beaching. But it wasn't his friends, and he's still awaiting the two hundred grand to make the buy. If you think it strange his telling me this, you don't know Bimini, where a stranger will tell you his life story and casually inform you he's into bestiality and proud of it.

Later that day, Marty and I take a stroll along the King's Highway, which runs beside the beach (the only other main road, the Queen's Highway, runs along the harbor; the names switch according to whether a king or queen rules England). Every ten yards or so, he stops to confer with one of the locals, who are no good at making runs. They only load the boats and make deals, which is what Bahamians do best. When it comes to making deliveries, that can wait until *mañana*.

Marty is a kingpin in the drug business, a member of the Rizzo family of New Brunswick, New Jersey. One of his nineteen uncles was pardoned by Tricky Dicky because he knew Sinatra, and Sinatra knew Agnew, et cetera, et cetera.

According to Marty, he spent six months at Foxhill Prison in Nassau because some cops on Andros raided his villa for five pounds of cocaine, which they never found. Subsequently, Marty took his Uzi down to the tavern where they hung out. He riddled the bar with bullets, shattering the splintered wood counter while the police lay panicked on the floor. Later, the cops got the drop on him, and one cop's revolver was shaking so badly Marty surrendered. Then, Andy got the drop on the cops, and he and Marty fled to the hills, where they held off a task force of sixty Bahamian CID agents for over two hours before surrendering.

Marty shared a cell with four Haitians, with one bucket to shit in and a long urinal running the length of the prison, no bunk, one meal of peas-and-rice a day, one shower a week, and sometimes no water for two days. He hired the best lawyer in Nassau, a cabinet member, to defend him and eventually got off for seventy-five grand bribe money.

Marty, who has done time in the States, explained prison was much nicer in the USA. The state of New Jersey spends fifteen thousand dollars annually on each prisoner. In the Bahamas, they don't spend shit! So no one worries about things like bail or probation. You can sit there till you rot for all they care.

Marty had money and connections, so he got out. But Andy was tried separately and didn't. Instead, he escaped while they were taking him in a bus from court to prison. He stole a cop's gun and made it to Paradise Island, where he forced a yachtsman at gunpoint to take him to Andros. There he phoned Marty, who flew him back to the States in his Piper Cub. Things like that happen to Marty a lot.

The day Marty was telling me this, CID agents arrested six Colombians loading a boat with bales of marijuana at the government dock in broad daylight. The rumor was they'd failed to deliver ten percent of the grass to the agents beforehand, so the feds confiscated it and would deal it wholesale at fifty dollars a pound.

A tourist lady was about to take a snapshot of the handcuffed Colombians, the bales of dope, and the four cigarette boats when an agent in a black jumpsuit and beret leveled his M-16 and said evenly, "No pictures." The reason for this, Marty informed me, was that by the time the Colombians came to trial there wouldn't *be* any evidence, so the Colombians would get off scot free, and the CID would pocket a small fortune.

A Columbian shook off his captors and dove into the water, still cuffed. The agents fired a warning shot over his head, and he dolphin-kicked back to the dock to be lifted out.

Marty, who resembles Paul Newman except for the tattoo of a naked lady on his right forearm, has a farm in the mountains outside Ocho Rios, Jamaica, where he harvests dope with the aid of four hundred Rastafarians. All are armed and have chain saws to clear the land, though at first it was pretty scary turning a mob of Rastas loose with chain saws when they're used to machetes.

When Marty was serving time at Foxhill in Nassau, the CIA came to visit and offered him a ticket out and lots of loot if he'd use his mad Rasta army to direct a revolution against the socialist government. Marty preferred the hell of Foxhill over being associated with the CIA, who he knew would use him up and spit him out. The

Bahamian government might be corrupt, but the corruption was on the surface where you could deal with it. Being a pirate, he chose to deal with the Bahamians.

Marty has a secret airfield in the mountains of Jamaica, with four Piper Cubs that deliver to the States. On arrival in south Florida, the bales are dumped out an open hatch onto isolated fields where trucks pick them up, making landings unnecessary. The first time they tried it Andy shoved a bale out, and it smashed the wing strut. They were forced to make a crash landing at Opa Locka Airport. Marty drove the truck onto the runway and picked up Andy and the pilot, leaving the dope and airplane behind.

The dope in Bimini was pirate dope, Marty explained— dope that had been ripped off or confiscated dope the law was selling wholesale. However, there was a scarcity of buyers since there'd been a number of recent rip-offs and smugglers were wary.

Bahamians rarely smuggle dope. Instead, they smuggle Haitians into the States because the penalty for smuggling aliens is only deportation back to the Bahamas. Marty told me a story about the time his Biminite compatriots Picolo and Boatie packed forty-five Haitians on a forty-two-foot Hatteras for delivery to the mainland. Instead of smuggling them into the States, they took 'em out to sea for six hours, delivered them back to the far side of South Bimini, then told them to walk two miles inland to a nonexistent Miami.

Marty had had two boats confiscated by the Coast Guard for smuggling Haitians. From then on he determined to use the cheapest boats available. There's no percentage in delivering thirty or forty Haitians at four hundred dollars a head, when one stands to lose a $150,000 boat.

All day long, Biminites deliver garbage bags full of dope in broad daylight, as if everyone is headed for the dump. Only, the real garbage is thrown out on the beautiful, white beaches.

One night a hundred or so CID agents invaded Alice Town, checking all the homes for dope, without search warrants. The Biminites were out on the streets and in the bars cursing the government, which was, after all, paid in drug money. It was the closest thing to a revolution I've ever seen on Bimini.

*

Behind the Hy Star, the new *Saturday Night Fever*-like disco, a drunken Colombian was checking out his new Smith & Wesson and accidentally fired off two rounds that passed through one Biminite's leg and another's foot.

The next afternoon, I saw Naman, the man who'd been shot in the leg, coming out of the free clinic. He explained he'd been so high on coke it was an hour before he realized he was wounded. As we talked, a party of Midwestern divers was eating their complimentary conch fritters and drinking their complimentary goombay smashes at Brown's.

*

Sports fishermen in forty-two-foot Hatteras yachts slaughter gigantic fish with the aid of about half a million dollars' worth of equipment, a two-hundred-dollar-a-day skipper, and two mates. Then they blast into dock, hang the slaughtered fish on scales, get even more roaring drunk, call all the women "cunts," eye all the Biminites and nonsports fishermen suspiciously, and call for more drinks till they pass out in their own vomit. The next day, they do it all over again after a hearty breakfast of Kellogg's Corn Flakes.

*

Marty and I spy a beauty in front of The Big Game Club as we're strolling down the Queen's Highway. She has tattoos all over her mostly exposed body and is carving a face in a coconut. It turns out she's from New Jersey, too, and her friends abandoned her on the island. The day before, they were in Nassau where she was raped— or nearly raped, she's not sure—by a black man, and she asks Marty if he's "carrying." Just like in the movies.

Marty has found himself a woman. Only later, after he took her up to *my* hotel room (Marty's staying with gangsters), she got insulted when he asked her to take a shower. Instead, she split. She ended up clinging possessively to one of the blacks she'd only hours before professed to despise.

But that's Bimini for you. A big part of the island's allure is the ready availability of black-white relationships. Bimini men will jump anything that walks. It's all pussy to them. Cast your gaze down the bar to the two fat, German lesbians who haven't changed their master-race, peasant outfits once in the week they've been here. Observe the four Biminites buying them drinks, hoping for a group grope. The hard sell, however, is out. Either they will or they won't. There's always someone who will, and a Biminite is friendly to conquest and nonconquest alike. It costs nothing to be friendly.

The next morning, I go diving with a group from Nebraska who are wearing about five thousand dollars' worth of dive equipment each. Some have compasses strapped to their wrists in case they decide to swim to Africa, along with vicious-looking Lloyd Bridges *Sea Hunt* knives strapped to their ankles for *mano a mano* combat with Jaws. All are attired in wet suits for thirty-foot dives in tropical waters. I feel naked since all I have is a pair of fins, mask, and snorkel. They eye me suspiciously. Maybe I'm from Lincoln instead of Omaha. Maybe they'd spotted me the night before doing the Bimini stomp with coal-black Peachy. They're drawing away from me as if I were a leper, whispering among themselves.

They figure it's the natives who're depraved, when it's the white people. In the end we all went diving, looked at thousands of colorful tropical fish, and cruised back to the dock.

*

Marty and I visit Bobby's, where Marty, like some great pope of the underworld, supplies the residents with coke, pot, and bail money. Whole families reside in Bobby's native shack—infants in diapers on a thread-bare couch, two whores from Freeport in the bedroom entertaining Mr. Bobby, the TV turned up full volume and the stereo blasting. Marty, two unfamiliar white men, and I are passing a joint in the living room, while Marty's henchman, Naman (who has somehow managed to mis-place two of Marty's $150,000 boats and stay alive), is in the kitchen attacking a Bimini chick who's giggling maniacally.

When Bobby steps out in his BVDs, he and Marty rem-inisce about their first meeting five years ago. Marty was "cooling out" around 4 A.M. outside Perry's Saloon, a native hangout that stays open all night, with a beat-up pool table, naked-lady pictures on the walls, and every-body smoking dope and drinking straight shots and beer. Marty was standing outside in a light drizzle, smoking a "number," when a car pulled up and Bobby stepped out with a .45 and shot a passing black man in the head. He spotted the ember of Marty's joint glowing faintly in the dark and pointed the gun at him. Marty said, "That ain't shit, man," and they're blood brothers for life. Marty helped Bobby dump the body where sharks would eat it, and Bobby called Marty the meanest "Conchy Joe" (white Bahamian) in the islands. Isn't friendship like that rare in this modern, computerized age?

*

The Martys and Bobbys of the world are the greediest people imaginable. Only, they don't think of it as money. They think of it as chips, and one can't amass enough chips because whoever has the most chips at the end of the game is the winner. Those are the stakes they play for, all or nothing. He who's not with me is agin' me. It's the largest capitalistic game in the universe. But if they fuck up, they're dead.

Marty claims in March he's going to take a month off and tour Europe, but you know he never will. Or if he does, he'll become involved in the same shit over there. The true gangster must constantly have his fix of the adrenaline rush of fragile mortality.

Anyway, that's Bimini. One minute you hate it; the next you love it. But it's always the same old Bimini. The natives never change and neither do the "seaweeds," which is what they call outsiders who drift up on their shores.

*

Ossie and I are sitting on the Bimini wall, facing the ocean. It's early evening, and the sun is sinking into the turquoise-blue ocean. Children in starched, blue school uniforms are passing, and Ossie, an island authority, tells me Biminites have always been involved in smuggling. In the '20s it was booze; later, "Chinee." Now it's dope and Haitians. Still, they despise Haitians. There are benches facing the ocean that have painted across the backs in huge, black letters, "Haitian, No."

As we speak, the CID has rounded up another six boat-loads of dope and has them at the government dock. Only this time, they've handcuffed the Colombians together so none will try to escape. One is a woman, and all are smoking cigarettes with manacled hands and smiling contentedly like this is nothing new. Ossie tells me it's practically a daily occurrence now and will be till the cops receive a bigger cut of the action.

On the Queen's Highway walks Pope Marty, bestowing his blessings on henchmen and nonhenchmen alike, generous with his largesse, a man with a name in this part of the world—for now, anyway, but not tomorrow. For what is tomorrow on an island where Hemingway's remembered not as a writer but as a drunken bully and anyone not born on the island, be he from Nassau, the States, or Haiti, is only a seaweed?

So Ossie and I share the Bimini wall while pedestrians and natives on bicycles flow past slowly, ever so slowly. The wind is blowing clean and pretty. Forty or so miles beyond the Gulf Stream sits Miami, where lights glow in evening time like beacons from a distant planet. . . .

Accident

≈

Roosters were crowing stridently when Accident rolled over on his broken, rusty spring-coiled bed and rubbed the sleep from his eyes. The evening before had been wash night at his mother's, so a freshly laundered pair of jeans and white t-shirt—with "Accident Coming" written on the front and "Accident Leaving" on the back—hung on wood pegs beside his cot. Accident threw on his clothes and went over to the chipped enamel basin to wash his face and hands. Then he swung open the rickety wood door and stepped outside. Bolting the entrance of his eight-by-ten-foot shack with a combination padlock, he headed for work.

The sun was a fiery, red ball on the edge of the pale blue horizon when Acci arrived at Brown's Hotel, a concrete block monstrosity that is the least of the Browns' three hotels, and began sweeping the pockmarked tile floor of the restaurant and adjoining bar.

"Take the garbage out to the truck, Acci," commanded his boss, Neville, from behind the rough wood bar.

Acci had loaded four garbage cans on the rusted bed of the ancient, blue Ford pickup when Neville slid behind the wheel and flipped the ignition. The engine stuttered and complained, bolts rattling ominously, before roaring to life. Acci rode in back with the garbage, and they were

Accident with *Bimini by the Sea* producer Ed Baatz

halfway to the dump when he spotted a Conchy Joe named David Warner walking down the King's Highway toward Brown's.

"Where's my money, Acci?" shouted Warner at the retreating truck.

Acci had borrowed fifteen dollars from a drunken Warner the day before and promised to pay him back before the seaplane took off at noon.

"Not to worry, Cap," shouted Acci through cupped palms. "I be back to the hotel with it in no time!"

Suppose I don't make it back until after his flight has left, thought Acci. What's fifteen bucks to a Conchy Joe? Five Kaliks at Brown's bar.

When Acci had dumped the garbage, he brushed his calloused palms on his jeans and turned to Neville. "My mama's ailing, and I need to visit with her awhile."

"It'll cost you some money. I don't pay you to visit your mama."

Acci nodded resignedly.

He spent the next four hours at the dimly red-lit Precious de Paris Club drinking up Warner's fifteen dollars. Around twelve-thirty, he stood up from the rickety

metal stool and walked down an uneven flight of wood
stairs to the dusty tar road.

*

It was a little before one when Acci lifted his broom and
finished sweeping the floor at Brown's with quick, staccato strokes. Then, he stepped out on the Queen's Highway
for a smoke. He'd just lit up when he saw Warner, bag in
hand, headed for Chalk's.

Damn Chalk's to hell, thought Acci. The flight must've
been delayed.

"Hey Accident, where's my fucking money?" demanded
Warner.

You can't bleed a stone, thought Acci, and he'll be gone
in thirty minutes.

He was about to empty his pockets for Warner's benefit
when Neville, who had walked out unnoticed and was
standing behind him, spoke up. "Acci owe you money,
mon?"

Warner nodded: "Fifteen bucks."

Without a word, Neville drew a thick wad of bills with a
rubber band around it out of his pants pocket and slapped

three crisp, colorful Bahamian five bills into Warner's waiting palm.

"Thanks," said Warner, stuffing the money into his khaki shorts and hurrying on his way. Better Bahamian money than no money at all, he thought.

Neville watched bemusedly as Acci's shoulders slumped and his face soured.

"You best be getting back to work, mon," he said. "So I can take the fifteen dollars you owe me out of your pay."

Island Hustle

≈

Through the years, J. B. must've tried to scam me a hundred or more times, but he never gave up trying. He was standing beside the Queen's Highway, a long line of polished conch shells on the uneven stone wall behind him, when Amanda and I passed.

"Hey, Cap, a beautiful shell for the beautiful lady?"

As usual, I ignored him.

A couple of years earlier, my friend Cap'n Dan was relaxing on his boat in the harbor when J. B. rowed up beside him with a load of fresh conch.

"Need anything, Cap? Conch, dope, a woman?"

Cap'n Dan experienced a sudden epiphany. "What would a hundred bucks buy me? I want the most beautiful woman on the island."

He drew a crisp U.S. hundred-dollar bill out of his billfold and handed it over.

"You can count on me, Cap!" exclaimed J. B., pocketing the bill and rowing hastily away.

For the next month or so, J. B. melted away like a phantom at the sight of Cap'n Dan, who breathed a deep sigh of relief.

*

But Amanda and I were only going to be on the island a couple of days scouting locations for a travel video, *Bimini by the Sea*, and a hundred dollars seemed an extravagant price to pay for a little peace and quiet.

*

That evening, Amanda and I met for drinks at the Angler Bar. Luckily for us, J. B. spent his nights in the Bimini jail for selling dope without greasing the proper palms—they turned him loose days to sweep the streets and hustle his meals.

But J. B. wasn't the only hustler on Bimini. Far from it! There was Festus, for example. Festus spent his evenings cadging drinks from seaweeds and propositioning any and every female—black, white, short, tall, thin, fat, young, old—on the island.

It wasn't long before Festus slithered over next to us at the bar. "Buy me a Kalik, Cap." Then to Amanda, who

Memory Ledge lookout before it was destroyed by storms

was twenty years my junior and must've appeared a tasty morsel ripe for the plucking: "Hi, my name is Nokia. My uncle, Ossie, owns this place." Then, to me: "Sir, what a lovely daughter you have!"

Festus changed his name constantly to prevent disgruntled seaweeds from tracking him down later, and Ossie was no more Festus's uncle than I was. But I let it pass. If Amanda were fool enough to go for Festus, so be it.

Sure enough, five or six goombay smashes later, she left to go for a ride on his scooter.

*

Amanda hadn't been gone long when I headed up to Perry's in Baileytown. The joint was jumping when I got there and located the only seat at the crowded bar.

"How's it going?" I asked Bonefish Baldwin, Bimini's most popular guide.

Bonefish grinned his trademark grin. "It's going. What's shaking with you, mon?"

"I'm scouting locations for a video about Bimini. Got any ideas?"

Before Bonefish could answer, a tiny, wizened elf of a black man seated on my right suddenly came alive. "Been out to Memory Ledge? It's where you see your past, present, and future. All at the same time."

I regarded him dubiously. "I've been coming to Bimini for over twenty years, and I never heard of Memory Ledge."

The man leaned over conspiratorially. "Not many sea-weeds have. It's not something we talk about to just any-body, but you're making a video, right?"

*

Skipping to the chase, I paid the elf a fifty-dollar find-er's fee and wound up in one of Bimini's ubiquitous cabs headed north on the Queen's Highway. At the north end of the North Island, we rolled to a grinding halt and got out. Memory Ledge consisted of a tiny, concrete gazebo at the end of a long, curving, aluminum-reinforced walk-way jutting out into the Gulf Stream. A full moon ghost-lit the dark Atlantic. I followed my guide out to the gaze-bo, while the cab waited.

"Lie down in the center and close your eyes."

I did as instructed.

"Sail with me now into the oceans of eternity . . ." the elf intoned in a soothing, hypnotic voice.

The next thing I knew, an indeterminate amount of time had passed, and I was alone on Memory Ledge. When I walked back to the cab, it was gone.

My mind was blank. Something might've happened, but I didn't know what. Had I seen the past, present, and future? Or was it just an elaborate scam?

I started the four-mile hike back to Alice Town.

*

Two or three hours later, I was stumbling down the Queen's Highway looking for an open bar when the Bird Lady fell into lock step behind me.

The Bird Lady must've weighed sixty pounds soaking wet, with pencil-thin, bird-like legs, and I never once heard her utter an intelligible word. Whether her condition was the result of drink, drugs, dementia, or some combination of the three, I don't know.

"Cawww . . . cawww . . ." she crowed like a hyperactive cockatoo. "Cawww . . . cawww . . ."

When I turned to go upstairs to my room at the Angler, she leapt aboard my back, matchstick arms tight about my neck, and refused to budge.

"Cawww . . . cawww . . ." she screeched. "Cawww . . . cawww . . ."

Was this her subtle way of propositioning me? Or had she lost what little was left of her mind? With some effort, I pulled her off my back, but she insisted on trailing me up three flights of stairs to my room.

"Cawww . . . cawww . . ." Then, plaintively: "Cawww? Cawww?"

I unlocked the door and squeezed past her into the room. Slamming the door, I locked it from the inside and slid a chair under the doorknob.

"Cawww . . . cawww . . ." Short pause. "Cawww . . . cawww . . ."

Finally I heard the steady pat-pat of her faint footfalls descending the stairs and fell gratefully into bed.

*

The next morning, I awoke with a horrendous hangover and stumbled over to Capt. Bob's for some medicinal grunt 'n' grits. Amanda was seated at a Formica-topped table, nursing a steaming cup of java, and I joined her.

I didn't ask what'd happened between Festus and her the night before. It was none of my business. "Not feeling too hot, heh?"

Amanda shook her head forlornly.

We ate our breakfast in silence, with me downing a half dozen or so glasses of water, and I paid the bill.

"A little grass might help ease the pain," said Amanda. "Know where we can get some?"

Grass isn't exactly my style, but I didn't say anything. If she wanted grass, I'd get it for her.

*

J. B. was standing in his usual spot when I approached him.

"Morning, Cap, buy a shell for the lovely lady?"

"Got any grass?" I asked.

J. B. raised a finger to his lips and checked out the road in both directions. "Twenty bucks a joint. Meet me across from Weech's dock in half an hour."

Thirty minutes later I was standing across from Weech's, but there was no sign of J. B.

Island time, I thought, settling in for a long wait.

But it was no more than five minutes before J. B. appeared with a furtive look, as if the whole island were in a conspiracy to keep him from selling me a joint.

He took a crumpled pack of Rothman's cigarettes out of his pants pocket and lit up. Then he handed me the pack. "The joint's inside."

I flipped open the pack. Sure enough, there was a raggedy-looking joint along with two regular cigarettes. I pocketed the pack and handed J. B. a twenty. Without so much as a word, he took the bill and ducked into an alley leading up to the beach road.

*

A little later, Amanda and I went up to my room to smoke the joint. We sat next to one another on the bed and lit up. Only instead of a marijuana cigarette, it was *real* grass—Bermuda grass.

"It figures," said Amanda like one who had learned a valuable lesson.

Twenty years of coming to the island, and I still didn't know any better. I started to laugh, and Amanda joined me. We laughed till we cried, as though J. B.'s "grass" had gotten us high, after all.

Rick

≈

Rick had flown the latest herd of New Agers over from Lauderdale and was showing them around Alice Town. A Vietnam-trained fighter pilot, he'd been flying to Bimini in his zebra-striped DC-3 for over twenty years.

Rick and the New Agers took the ferry from South Bimini, where the tiny, potholed airstrip was, to the government dock and were eating dinner at the Red Lion when Ashley joined them. Ashley, with Eastern beard and fine-featured Carib Indian face, was Bimini's resident guru, a school teacher-poet-herb doctor who was educated at Harvard and knew the locations of the alleged remnants of the lost continent of Atlantis.

Rick

Another must-see for the Atlantis group was the notorious concrete ship, the *Sapona*, a former rum-running vessel that had been built during World War I and ran aground off Bimini in a storm during prohibition.

On December 5, 1945, five Avenger torpedo bombers left to fly a practice torpedo run over the *Sapona*. Shortly thereafter, the control tower received an urgent message from the flight leader reporting that they couldn't see land, couldn't be sure of any direction, and that even the ocean didn't look as it should. Radio contact grew steadily worse. The tower picked up one pilot saying his instruments were "going crazy."

A rescue mission was launched. A giant Martin Mariner flying boat, with a crew of thirteen, took off toward the last reported position of the flight. Twenty-three minutes later, the sky to the east was lit by a bright orange flash.

None of the aircraft was seen again.

Adherents of UFOs and the Devil's Triangle believe the aircraft entered a time warp or were abducted by aliens.

*

After dinner, the New Agers trooped over to the Angler, where Rick proceeded to get seriously drunk on goombay smashes while his charges perused the newspaper and magazine clippings about Bimini as Atlantis in plastic frames on the walls.

A meeting of Hemingway scholars was taking place on the island, and they mingled uneasily with the New Agers. Oil and water. Rationalists versus mystics. Obsessed in turn with the Great Writer and Edgar Cayce, the Sleeping

Prophet, who predicted remnants of Atlantis would be discovered off Bimini.

Ashley, who had stepped out back to toke a doobie, was
hawking his *History of Bimini*, with rundowns on
Hemingway and Atlantis, when his uncle Picolo Pete
entered the Angler. Picolo was to Hemingway scholars
what Ashley was to New Agers—a man who had known
and been written up by Papa himself.

The Hemingway crowd gathered around Picolo off the
lobby in the Hemingway Room—photos of E. H. on
Bimini, including one of him machine-gunning sharks off
Brown's Dock, with quotes from his works underneath—
and listened as he spun elaborate fantasies about his and
E. H.'s adventures.

Meanwhile Rick had met a girl at the bar. Her name was
Doris, and she'd been abandoned by a fickle lover who had
sailed off to parts unknown with another girl.

Rick, like his compadrés Boatie and Cap'n Dan, was
something of a womanizer, and he specialized in "boat
girls"—women who drifted from island to island on the
vessels of various lovers, island currency as exchangeable as
the drugs and liquor they used to stay afloat.

High winds and bad weather had kept the usual hard-drinking boating crowd away, and Devil was preparing to close the bar when there was a staccato series of loud pops from outside. The racket came from the ocean side, and everyone rushed out to the beach to see what was going on.

Skimming just above the waves, less than a hundred yards from shore, was a disc-shaped flying vessel with alternating blue and red lights illuminating its translucent interior. Before the amazed eyes of fifty or so spectators, it sliced silently into the water, lights blinking on and off from beneath the murky depths, only to reappear seconds later and reverse direction. One final zigzag across the moonless sky, and it was gone!

The New Agers nodded their heads knowingly, while the Hemingway scholars maintained it was mass hypnotism.

Devil, who had seen similar displays in the past, walked casually back to the bar to finish counting the night's receipts as Rick turned with fuzzy eyes and open mouth to Doris, who had vanished.

One moment, she was at his side; the next, she wasn't.

Maybe she was an alien boat girl, thought Rick. A sign from Cayce himself, whose only trip outside the States was to search for buried treasure on Bimini.

Rick decided to call it a night and sleep alone.

Looking for
Atlantis

≈

My search for Atlantis off Bimini began at Cassadaga, in central Florida. The tiny village of Cassadaga is like New England in appearance, with white clapboard cottages and narrow, shaded streets. Reminiscent of the subtropics is the prolific Spanish moss bearding tall, stately oaks. The first thing you notice is the quiet. Aside from the twittering of jays and rustling of squirrels in the trees, there's little to disturb the peace. Occasionally, one passes groups of visitors, many of them elderly with an almost equal number of middle-aged women and a smattering of young couples chatting in low, subdued voices as though in church. The tags on the cars parked along the road proclaim most to be from up north, especially the Midwest.

The Spiritualist camp is laid out in a hilly square with four small, tree-filled parks that have names like Healing Tree around two dark green lakes, Lake Colby and Spirit Pond. Nine short roads at right angles to Stevens Street, the main drag, are lined with cottages inhabited by more than forty certified mediums. Small wood signs out front list the names of the residents. Many of the names are preceded by the title, Reverend. Aside from the mediums' homes, the camp consists of the Cassadaga Hotel, a white stucco building with a long, wraparound, stone porch, built in 1922. Its dimly lit lobby is decorated with a beshawled Victorian piano and photographs of famous mediums who have visited. To the right side of the hotel is the Andrew Jackson Davis meeting hall (named after a famous nineteenth-century medium and author of *The Principles of Nature*). It's a whitewashed wood building resembling an army barracks and contains meeting rooms and a bookstore specializing in mystic and Spiritualist literature. Appointments with mediums can be made there.

Cassadaga was founded on January 3, 1895, when Reverend William Colby donated thirty-five acres of land in Volusia County to the Southern Spiritualist Camp Meeting Association.

The seeds leading to this decision were planted when, twenty years earlier, twenty-seven-year-old Colby held a séance at Lake Mills, Iowa. During this séance, Colby purportedly heard an urgent message from his Indian spirit guide, Seneca, who told him to head for Eau Claire, Wisconsin, to meet with a fellow Spiritualist named T. D. Giddings. The next morning, Colby traveled to Giddings's home in Eau Claire. Both men were told by Seneca to travel to Florida, where a Congress of Spirits had decided a Spiritualist camp was to be established.

Colby and Giddings, along with Giddings's family, traveled by rail to Jacksonville and by steamboat up the St. Johns River to Blue Springs. Seneca had informed them the camp was to be in the vicinity of Blue Springs "on high pine bluffs overlooking a chain of silvery lakes." In Blue Springs, Seneca made contact again and told them to follow his instructions. The two men then "followed a footpath for a little distance, then straight through the deep forest. They went for several miles, until at last . . . they viewed the promised land: the high bluffs, the lake, the lay of the land, everything was found exactly as it had been described by Seneca before leaving Wisconsin."

For reasons unknown, Colby did nothing to establish the camp he had been sent to create. Instead, for the next eighteen years he operated a dairy farm. In 1893, another Spiritualist named Rowley attempted to establish a camp in nearby Winter Park. A number of prominent Spiritualists arrived from up north. Unimpressed with Rowley, they met with Colby. With his encouragement, they established the camp on his property.

Communicating directly with ghostly presences was a common occurrence at Cassadaga before the '60s. According to an eyewitness account in Robert Harrold's *Cassadaga*:

> With the medium inside (a wood closet) and the guard posted, all lights would be turned off . . . From out of the pitch darkness, a swirl would materialize. It would appear to come from the cabinet. Gradually, it would form into a full length human form. It would be white, yet appear to be almost transparent, ghostly. . . .

Cassadaga

This materialized spirit would walk in front of [the spectators] and speak to them. Oftentimes the spirit would be known to someone in the room, a brother who had died, a husband, a sister. And more often than not, the spirit would have personal messages for all those present, either from the spirit itself or its companions in the World of Spirit.

Starting in the '60s, the mediums of Cassadaga—perhaps put off by accusations of trickery and attempted exposés—resorted to a more subtle form of communication with the dead. Today, the person seeking information sits on a comfortable chair in a dimly lit room. A medium sits opposite and gives what is known as a "reading."

I had two readings at Cassadaga.

My first reading was given by a woman in her mid-forties with a slight British accent. A sign above the front door read "No Smoking." Her small reading room was tastefully decorated with Indian artifacts and paintings, including an oil portrait of an Indian maiden who is her spirit guide.

She asked me to place my palms on top of hers so she could feel my "vibrations." She leaned back in her armchair and went into a trance. Several minutes passed, during which the only sound was the steady swish, swish of the fan. Finally, she opened her eyes. "The first image I had was of you as a bull grazing alone in a field. You're content just to graze and not charge anyone. This image symbolizes the fact that relationship-wise, you're no longer leading with your heart. You've learned the virtue of patience and are awaiting the right opportunity. Does this mean anything to you?"

I nodded my head yes.

"It certainly does," I thought to myself. However, the skeptic in me couldn't help adding, me and about a billion other people!

There followed more of this imaging: a baby eagle learning to fly, a golf ball sailing straight down a fairway, a tightrope walker finding the correct balance.

At the end of the reading, she asked if there were anyone who'd passed on whom I would care to contact.

"Jim Turner," I said.

Jim Turner was a relative of mine who had served as high-sheriff of a rural Florida county for over twenty years.

"I see a good ole boy leaning against a pick-up truck, drinking a beer. He's wearing some kind of uniform and has a badge. He says he's here to protect you, to make sure no one gives you any trouble. Does that make sense?"

"Jim was an old man when I knew him, and he drank Scotch. But that might have been a somewhat accurate picture of him when he was younger, especially the part about the badge on his uniform and his protecting me. After all, he *was* a sheriff."

"Hold on a minute." She closed her eyes and placed her hand to her forehead. "Someone else is coming through. She's a little old lady, less than five feet tall. She lived to be very old, late eighties or early nineties. And she's wearing a pair of thick glasses like she can hardly see. She says she wants to shake you sometime. 'Loosen up,' she says. Does that make any sense to you?"

"The lady you describe bears a striking resemblance to my grandmother on my mother's side. Especially the part about her height and the glasses. And the fact she wants to shake me. It was one of her favorite expressions when she was mad with me."

But then, a lot of people have a grandmother who would fit that description, piped up the skeptic in me. Still, there was the part about wanting to shake me. It *was* one of her favorite expressions when she was angry.

After all, it only takes one white crow to disprove all crows are black!

My second reading was given by a short, nondescript man in his mid-forties. When we shook hands, I detected a vague odor of tobacco and alcohol about his person. His reading room was overheated, dimly lit, and furnished in early Sears Roebuck. We took seats opposite one another, separated by a coffee table covered with different-sized healing crystals.

According to him, he could read my vibrations by interpreting colors he perceived as auras about my person. Leaning back on the sofa, he placed his hands to his temples and delivered a series of generalizations that were, more or less, correct. His first direct hit was the fact that I'm a writer.

"Someday soon," he said, "you'll make travel videos."

"Travel videos . . . " I echoed incredulously. When I thought of videos, I thought of music videos on MTV. "Are you sure you don't mean films or, better yet, novels?"

He shook his head no. "I see you working with friends on videos."

"I can't see it."

But, he was adamant. "You will."

Two years later, I did.

*

It started when an artist friend read a short story of mine.

"This would make a great movie!" he exclaimed.

I agreed, but so what? Movies cost millions of dollars to make, and I'd never had any luck peddling screenplays.

But my friend had a friend who produced documentaries for PBS at Gainesville, Florida. Between the three of us, we managed to make a forty-four-minute video about my deceased relative, High-Sheriff Jim Turner and the New Year's Day 1923 Black Massacre at Rosewood, Florida. The video certainly didn't win any awards, but it was cheap enough to make and got shown at some fairly prestigious film festivals.

At least we had our foot in the door.

The next November, following a screening of our video at the Ft. Lauderdale Film Festival, I flew over to Bimini. I hadn't been there long before an idea struck me. Why not make a video about Bimini? After all, I'd been going over there for twenty years and was familiar with its colorful history.

It was a natural.

I went to see my friend Ashley Saunders, an island poet, teacher, and herb doctor, who had written a history of the island. At Ashley's place, I spotted a copy of the Cayce Foundation's house organ, *Venture Inward.*

On the cover was an aerial photograph of huge sand mounds shaped like various kinds of fish, including a lemon shark. According to the article inside, the mounds had been sighted on East Bimini in 1989 by a low-flying aircraft. On closer examination, the mounds turned out to be five hundred feet long and ten feet high, surrounded by a sand beach and kept in place for centuries by a mangrove forest. According to Ashley, six generations of Biminites have known about the sculptures, and they appeared on early nautical charts. How they knew remains a mystery since they can be identified only from the air.

That afternoon, I was having lunch when a lady walked by carrying the same issue of *Venture Inward* I'd seen earlier. Naturally, I asked where she got it. She explained she and some others were taking part in a psychic reunion. According to her, they had all spent "previous lives" on Bimini when it was a part of the lost continent of Atlantis over ten thousand years ago. The sand mounds played a part in their religious observances.

The plot was thickening.

Later, I met with Joan Hanley, leader of the Atlantis group. Joan had hired a diver from Lauderdale to video-tape an "underwater Atlantian road," a freshwater heal-ing spring, and the sand sculptures. She wanted to know what had drawn me to Bimini for twenty years. I got the feeling she considered me a fellow Atlantian. At any rate, I was welcome to use some of the tape in my video if I liked.

Things were falling into place.

Back home in Florida, I began my research.

Between 1923 and 1944, the famous healer and psy-chic Edgar Cayce, under hypnosis, made numerous ref-erences to Atlantis. In 1926, he visited Bimini in search of pirate treasure that was never recovered, his only trip out of the U.S.

In 1932, Cayce stated, "The position the continent of Atlantis occupied is between the Gulf of Mexico on one hand and the Mediterranean on the other. . . . The British West Indies, including the Bahamas, are a por-tion. . . . If a geological survey would be made . . . in Bimini . . . these may yet be determined."

In 1933, Cayce said, "As indicated, the records as to constructing same are in three places in the Earth. . . .

In the sunken portion of Atlantis, or Poseida, where a portion of the temples may yet be discovered under the slime of ages of seawater—near what is known as Bimini. . . ."

In 1940, Cayce predicted evidence that the Atlantian island of Poseida would appear: "expect it in '68 or '69. It will happen in the area of the Bahamas."

In 1968, an unusual formation of stones was spotted by a low-flying plane, and Dr. J. Manson Valentine, curator of the Science Museum of Miami, was taken there by a local fishing guide, Bonefish Sam. Valentine was assisted in his explorations by underwater explorer Dimitri Ribicoff, who provided underwater photographic equipment for taking wide-angle photographs. Together, they took photos of what came to be known as the "Bimini Road."

The Bimini Road is a five-hundred-foot structure of symmetrical stones, the largest of which measure sixteen square feet. Valentine and Ribicoff came to the conclusion the structure is the work of ancient man, a dike, perhaps, or a docking facility for antediluvian vessels. Though covered with sand and silt, the stones are plainly visible and form an underwater *U*. Three lines of

Edgar Cayce

stones resembling piers protrude some seventy-five feet from the base of the *U*. The blocks are limestone and have been submerged for six to ten thousand years.

According to Ribicoff, who has explored similar underwater sites in the Mediterranean and elsewhere, the Bimini Road is evidence of a highly advanced, seagoing civilization that is identical in design to similar underwater sites in the Mediterranean.

Investigation of the road has produced two further artifacts: a tongue-and-groove building block fragment and a highly stylized animal head, a giant feline, worked from marble that is not native to the island. Neither of these finds bears any relation to a known Mesoamerican culture.

In one of Cayce's Bimini sessions, he predicted "healing springs," freshwater springs with miraculous healing powers, would someday be discovered on the island.

Biminites have known of a freshwater spring with supposed healing powers, called the "Healing Hole," for generations, but it wasn't until 1974 that Ernest Hemingway's younger brother, Leicester, was taken to where it's located among the mangroves on East Bimini. According to Hemingway, water from the spring healed the skin cancer on his forearms and another friend's lumbago. He took samples of it to the University of Miami to be analyzed, and they determined that it contained an extremely high lithium content. Lithium is used to treat manic depression.

My research done, I returned to the island with a film crew.

Once again, it was as if some psychic force were bringing things together. A particularly worrisome crewmember quit for no apparent reason. A boat was volunteered for ocean shooting, and another boat appeared at the right instant to provide a picture-perfect silhouette against an island sunset. An unscheduled Hemingway look-alike appeared just when he was needed. We'd no sooner planned a shot than things fell into place without effort.

Back home, things continued to happen. A PBS special on Adam Clayton Powell provided some much-needed Bimini footage of him. An Atlantis documentary on TV revealed a piece of esoteric information for which we had been desperately searching. We found the famous photo of Gary Hart, Donna Rice, and friends hanging in the lobby of the Compleat Angler, a poignant memento of Hart's fall from presidential grace. A video and film marketing agent in Beverly Hills, California, expressed an interest in our video. She learned of our project through an anonymous pen pal correspondence with the soldier son of our producer, who had been in Saudi Arabia during Desert Storm.

Strangest of all, a friend of mine "accidentally" received a flyer addressed to his ex-wife of five years at his business address. The flyer was from a San Diego travel agency and advertised a weeklong Atlantis seminar on Bimini. The seminar involved the Cayce Foundation, and two of the featured speakers were our friends Ashley Saunders and Joan Hanley. Again, it was as if some force were guiding us. We decided to premiere our video on Bimini at the same time as the Atlantis seminar.

In the meantime, the director, Alan, and I began rewriting the script, which we titled *Bimini by the Sea*. For one of the few times in my life, I felt totally in sync with someone. It was as if Al and I were two sides of the same personality.

When we were done, we set about looking for a narrator. Al had worked with David Ogden Stiers—the noted character actor who played Major Charles Winchester on the TV series *M.A.S.H.* and would sound good reciting the phone book. Stiers agreed to narrate the video, and

Al flew out to his home in Eugene, Oregon, to record him.

The sound track done, we rented editing equipment and worked day and night for a week putting the piece together. The rapport we shared was uncanny. One of us need only open his mouth before the other knew what he was about to say. One night, I dreamed Al and I were brothers in a previous life.

The final editing was done at Universal Studios in Orlando. Our producer, Ed, is a computer freak, and he was wide-eyed when he saw the millions of dollars' worth of technical equipment at our disposal. "Wow! Can you believe this?" he kept whispering in my ear, as Al directed the Universal technicians.

The video completed, we flew over to Bimini for our premiere. We screened it at the Bimini Breeze, a local bar. When it was over, we got a standing ovation from the locals. A dozen or so natives began pushing money on us wanting to buy a copy on the spot!

The trail had led to its destination, shaking my skepticism to a degree that probably has won the approval of my grandmother!

Boatie

≈

oatie awoke from his usual dream about women. He threw off the blanket and felt between his thighs, but no hardness was there. In his sleep, he'd been plowing a dense field of black, white, and oriental women, but the dream of life was different.

Boatie rolled off his bunk and went up on deck. It was a clear, cool morning with the wind blowing in briskly from the north-northwest. He examined his dark face in the cracked mirror mounted next to the helm. He was a handsome devil, all right—never mind the beginning of crow's-feet about his sparkling, brown eyes or the retouched hair and Fu Manchu mustache. Women loved him for his innocence as much as his looks. The act of lovemaking was a constant joy to him, something fresh and new, never tire-some.

Until recently, that is. It started with a dark-haired sea-weed named Laura.

Laura was a Manhattan model on the island for a fash-ion shoot, and they'd met at the Island House bar. She was shooting pool in back with a gay photographer when Boatie entered and took a seat at the hardwood bar. He was driving his cab that night, but things were even slow-er than usual.

The photographer was the first to notice Boatie, accus-tomed as he was to seeking out "rough trade" wherever he went. But Boatie ignored him and locked eyes with Laura. It wasn't long before the three of them were playing pool. Several games and many drinks later, Boatie and Laura left the photographer alone and drove back to his boat.

Everything went fine that first night. Since Laura had a month off between shoots, she decided to move aboard. Boatie had never let a girl live with him—even for a week. But Laura was different.

Boatie was used to taking the lead in lovemaking, but Laura turned the tables on him. For two days and nights, she was the aggressor, demanding and getting from Boatie the rapt devotion of a love slave. On the third morning, it happened. For the first time in his life, Boatie was unable to get it up. Rum . . . marijuana . . . cocaine . . . nothing worked.

As for Laura, she said nothing. Just lay on the deck, beautiful in her nakedness, like some pagan love goddess beyond the reach of mortal passion.

Maybe if he got away awhile, thought Boatie, spent some time alone . . .

Boatie left Laura, silent as the Sphinx, and went to the Island House for a drink. The Dolphins were playing the Cowboys on the wide-screen TV, and he tried to concentrate on the game. But it was no use. He felt violated, used, like a hairless Samson!

The gay photographer was shooting pool with Benjamin, one of a half-dozen or so gay Biminites, and Boatie tried to ignore them. After a half-hour or so of listless pool, the photographer sidled up to Boatie at the bar.

"How's it going with Laura?" he asked with a sly, knowing smile.

"All right," said Boatie, turning away and staring out the open door into the white-hot glare.

"Well, tell her I'm still here. Maybe the four of us can double date some time."

Something about the way he said it made Boatie uncomfortable, but he held his tongue. When he returned to his boat, he didn't mention the photographer's invitation to Laura.

Things went downhill from there. Try as he might, Boatie still couldn't get it up, and Laura's constant nakedness was a standing reproach.

Finally, without so much as a word, Laura left the island.

*

After that, every woman Boatie met was a potential Laura. Even the easily pleased island women became challenges in his mind. When he wasn't driving the cab, he spent his time drinking rum and watching sports on TV.

One night, Boatie was at the Island House, watching the Magic slaughter the Heat, when Cap'n Dan drew up the heavy wood bench beside his.

"How's it hanging, Boat Man? Knocking back much pussy?"

Boatie emitted a noncommittal grunt.

Cap'n Dan grinned. "Eyes getting bigger than your pecker, heh? Happens to the best of us." Ordering a round of rum and Cokes, he reached in the pocket of his grease-stained khaki shorts and brought out a vial of yellow pills. "Just swallow one of these beauties an hour before fucking, and you'll be as thick and hard as a bang stick."

Sure enough, that same week, Boatie made love to Doris, a semiattractive boat girl from Des Moines. Doris wanted to move aboard, but Boatie had learned a valuable lesson. From here on out, it was strictly casual sex for the Boat Man.

An Island
Romance

≈

Afternoon delight
Cocktails and moonlit nights
That dreamy look in your eye
Give me a tropical contact high.
                    Beach Boys, "Kokomo"

Her name was Virginia. . . .
I was married at the time, but my wife was
back in Florida, so I was on Bimini palling
around with a New Orleans Jew named Marty
whose family manufactured kosher hot dogs.

Marty had recently broken up with his girlfriend of three years, a former Miss Louisiana, and morose doesn't begin to describe his demeanor.

He was a good-looking, personable guy, and several of the island girls would have given him a tumble. But Marty didn't want anything to do with them, not even a quickie. His girlfriend had gone to Hollywood to become a movie star, and Marty's heart went with her.

One evening, Marty and I were bemoaning his fate over a couple of goombay smashes when two girls from stateside entered the Angler and sat down at the bar. They were four or five years older, around thirty, blonde and not beautiful, but attractive enough in a vaguely bohemian way.

Or at least, that's the way I saw it. Marty ignored them completely. Perhaps that's what drew them to us. Marty's indifference. Women are often attracted to the brooding, Lord Byron type, and Marty was nothing if not Byronic.

Virginia and Jill were their names. Virginia was recently divorced from a wealthy Arab and lived in Miami. Jill was a friend of hers from London. They'd flown over to Bimini for a holiday and to get away from Virginia's jealous ex.

It's funny how things will just click. You can search the world over for something and never find it. But the minute you stop looking, it'll fall in your lap. At that point in my life, I was in love with the concept of womanhood, not any one particular woman, and mysterious blondes on a happy-go-lucky tropical isle were just my cup of tea.

To make a long story short, I paired up with Virginia, and Marty paired up with Jill. We danced to the infectious island music and the mellow voice of Barry White and drank exotic rum concoctions in smoky, romantic dives with sand floors and rickety pool tables.

Later, like Bogart and Bacall, Virginia and I made love in the room where Hemingway wrote much of *To Have and Have Not*, and I experienced for the first time the magic of a woman's full-blown orgasm.

But it wasn't the lovemaking so much as the atmosphere. All my short life I'd wanted to experience an exotic-locale romance with a mysterious blonde like in the movies.

Never mind the fact I was betraying my wife. Anything for adventure in those days.

For Marty, it was different. His romance with Jill was at best a diversion. Something to help him get over his lost love. Girls were attracted to Marty like bees to honey, and this was just another in a long string of often reluctant conquests on his part.

And so it went in what were perhaps the four most romantic days of my life. There were tropical moonlight and nude swims and long, lazy afternoons spent making love.

Of course, Virginia and I knew next to nothing about each other. It was better that way. The dearth of personal knowledge was filled in by my vivid imagination.

Marty and I were drug smugglers on Bimini to pick up a load for delivery back to the states. Virginia was the beautiful but deadly *femme fatale* destined to come between us. Secondary characters based on island acquaintances included the gay Anglican priest and his choirboy lover.

My fantasy found form in a not-very-well-written James M. Cain/Dashiell Hammett-type thriller. But for now I was living the story in my head—a totally self-absorbed, would-be writer in love with a romantic illusion of his own creation. It had all the elements of a bad sitcom.

The same scenario would repeat itself several times in the future—the protagonists would all be blondes—but never with the same purity. It was an addiction, really, like heroin or cocaine or first and best love.

And yet . . .

There was something *realer* than so-called real life in my fantasy. For most people, life consists of getting up, working or playing, or both, then going to bed. I glimpsed a broader horizon, but my vision hadn't yet matured into something grander, more spiritual.

Years later, after studying the work of mystic-healer Edgar Cayce, I had a dream.

In the dream, I was in a boat on an endless ocean and caught a fish. When I tried to cram the fish into a cooler, it turned into a squirming rabbit and wouldn't fit.

The next day, I was reading a book of Cayce's dream interpretations and ran across the exact same dream experienced by a client of his during the '20s! According to Cayce, the ocean represents the sea of life, and the fish represents spirituality, as in early Christianity. The rabbit, of course, represents sex. The fish's turning into a rabbit symbolizes the fact that I was sublimating my need for God into a frantic quest for the perfect lover.

In other words, I was mistaking sex for salvation.

So I wasn't like Marty. My destiny wasn't to return home and work at the family business. Even then, I was an artist, and an artist has to blend in everywhere but belong nowhere. Like a conman or crook, he's a perpetual outsider, chameleon-like enough to pass through the different levels of society at will.

Eventually the girls left, and Marty and I were alone on the island. Like I said, it was no big deal to Marty. Ice broken, it wasn't long before he engaged in an even more casual affair with a bisexual French girl on a sailboat.

But I was smitten. Nothing would do but that I hook up with Virginia again. Only, when I rang her Miami number on my return home, it'd been disconnected.

For days, I mooned around listlessly, until my wife wanted to know what was wrong. Sagittarius that I am, I told her.

And that was the beginning of the end of that.

A couple of years passed, and we were divorced. The next year, Marty married a nice Jewish girl from Jacksonville whom my ex-wife had introduced him to.

Ten more years passed, and I was walking the beach on Bimini with my girlfriend. In all innocence, I told her about Virginia. Her mouth dropped open in horror! As luck would have it, Virginia had been her best friend growing up in Miami. Later, she'd gone into law and become a judge of juvenile court (how romantic). Still later, she stole my girlfriend's husband. In other words, she was my girlfriend's ex-husband's present wife!

And that was the beginning of the end of that.

Another ten years passed, and I heard Virginia was again divorced. I gave her a ring. Sure, she remembered me. She even had a photo of the four of us on Bimini. Only, her lover of five years had just died, and she was busy making funeral arrangements. Could I call again next week?

And that was the end of that.

Moral: Island romances are for islands.

Cap'n Dan

≈

Cap'n Dan had been crossing over to Bimini since he'd burnt his draft card and fled the States during the Vietnam war. Smuggling drugs, and later Haitians and other illegal aliens into the States, with his partners Picolo and Boatie was once his trade. Now the closest he came to danger was possibly impaling his hand with the gaffing hook when he brought some seaweed's marlin alongside the boat.

Cap'n Dan and his woman of the moment, Doris, were strolling north on the King's Highway alongside the chalky blue sea when the uneven pavement ended in a dirt path at the Rockwell property.

Through the years, this square-mile property on a two-square-mile island had belonged to George Lyon, Sr., inventor of the hubcap, who entertained the likes of Judy Garland and Frank Sinatra in his *Dr. No,* vessel-shaped home, with a roller skating rink that took up the entire third story. After Lyon's death in 1961, the estate was bought by the Rockwell Tool Corporation, manufacturer of missiles and rockets, as a getaway for clients and management. Now it belonged to a Cuban real estate syndicate from Miami, who were denuding it of Australian pines and palms and destroying the ecology with heavy equipment to build condos that nobody would buy.

Cap'n Dan and Doris skirted the sagging chain-link fence, the gateway to which was left unlocked, and walked north on the blindingly white, coral-sand beach. They

Cap'n Dan

hadn't walked a quarter-mile when they spotted a golf cart with a large, red-faced white man behind the wheel, weaving toward them through the few remaining trees.

As the cart drew nearer, Cap'n Dan recognized Chuck McGrew, governor of Florida, a rock-hard Republican who skewered the liberal opposition with deadly wit and a William F. Buckley vocabulary.

McGrew rolled silently up to them. "Where the hell d'ya think you're going?"

"To the north end of the island," Cap'n Dan said calmly.

McGrew leered at Doris. "Well, you're trespassing on private property, sonny!"

"No harm intended, Guv."

Before Cap'n Dan could say another word, McGrew reached into his navy blue windbreaker and pulled out a chrome-plated .45 automatic.

"You better leave. Now!"

Politicians! Cap'n Dan recalled the days when he drank with exiled Harlem congressman Adam Clayton Powell at the End of the World Saloon. Powell was a charming scoundrel who drank scotch and milk for his ulcer's sake and railed against the white establishment, members of

Adam Clayton Powell

which were often secretly his best friends and chief allies, for expelling him from Congress.

Politicians and smugglers have a lot in common, thought Cap'n Dan. Amorality, blind respect for the power of the buck, blatant disregard for the public. But smugglers are more honest. They deceive no one, including themselves, that they're knights in shining armor.

"Don't wave that gun around, Guv," warned Cap'n Dan. "You're liable to hurt yourself."

McGrew waved the gun menacingly. "Damn hippies!"

With one fluid movement, Cap'n Dan stepped up to McGrew's side and cold-cocked him with a sucker punch to his balding head. McGrew drooped woozily forward, forehead to steering wheel. Cap'n Dan casually lifted the gun and tossed it over his shoulder into the sea.

"That oughta hold him for awhile," said Cap'n Dan, rejoining Doris.

Doris nodded, and they continued their walk up the deserted beach. At journey's end, they disrobed and made love on a beach towel.

Later, when the governor came to, he didn't remember a thing. Stomping on the accelerator, he drove back to the Rockwell house for another scotch and water before breakfast.

The King of Bimini

≈

Ossie Brown was dead—victim of a crack-head Haitian who broke into his house to steal the daily bar receipts.

The Browns were the Bimini equivalent of the Rockefellers. They owned, among other things, a cargo ship, three hotels and bars, a couple of restaurants, two marinas, and choice real estate.

During the '30s, Captain Brown, the family patriarch, was the butler at the Compleat Angler. At that time, it belonged to Mrs. Helen Duncombe, a proper Brit who was married to the crown-appointed commissioner. Tea at four. Dinner at eight. It was a schedule that never varied, and Mrs. Duncombe locked the front door at ten sharp, much to the chagrin of a drunken Hemingway, who was forced to climb in a window and be led upstairs to bed by Brown.

In his spare time, Captain Brown was a rumrunner. Unlike most Biminites, he was trustworthy and dependable and soon owned a fleet of mob-sponsored boats that serviced Miami and south Florida.

As for Brown's offspring, his eldest son, Spencer, skippered the cargo ship back and forth to Miami. The second in line, Neville, ran the old, run-down Brown's Hotel. His third son, Julian, was a gambler and smuggler who, unlike his father, spent time in federal prison in Pensacola with Watergate conspirator Howard Hunt. In addition, there were two daughters who ran the marinas, and an illegitimate son who rented skiffs to seaweeds.

But Brown's youngest son, Oswald, was the apple of his eye. Following four years at Howard University in D.C., Ossie came home, and his father turned over management of the Compleat Angler, the jewel in his crown, to him. (Brown had bought the Angler when Mrs. Duncombe returned to England on the eve of Bahamian independence in 1972.)

At first, Ossie ran the Angler Bar, the chief moneymaker of the Brown empire, in typical island fashion, with frequent free drinks and running tabs for friends.

It was around this time that David Warner, on his first trip to the island in '72, met Ossie. Warner had read Hemingway's *Islands in the Stream* and wanted to be a writer himself.

Bimini was for him a sort of fairyland, a subtropical paradise where everyone did as he pleased—got drunk, took drugs, chased "womens" (as Hemingway called them), and raised hell in general—with no judgment call. And the Angler Bar was the center of activity.

Devil bartended and spun yarns; Boatie chased women; Picolo sang and played the banjo; Ashley recited his island poetry; Cap'n Dan cut drug deals; Rick, the pilot, shepherded the latest herd of New Agers over to explore the alleged remnants of Atlantis; and Accident acted the fool in general.

But Ossie was Warner's closest island friend. Especially on those magical nights when he closed the bar early, and there'd be just the two of them sitting at the dimly lit, hard Abaco-pine bar, sharing a bottle of Tangueray gin with limes and tonic.

Ossie Brown sitting in the courtyard of the Compleat Angler

One night, they were seated thus when there was a staccato series of sharp cracks like a bowling ball bouncing down the three flights of stairs.

"What the hell is that?" exclaimed Warner.

Ossie smiled his faint, beatific smile. "Mrs. Duncombe . . ."

"Isn't she dead?"

Ossie nodded. "Her spirit disapproves of what's going on in here. The drugs and Biminites dancing with white girls."

For Warner, Mrs. Duncombe symbolized the lost British Empire—stiff upper lip and stately decorum where everybody knew his place—and he was concerned that Ossie might be offended if he carried the conversation further. But Warner needn't have worried. Ossie, like most Biminites, was no revolutionary. He was a firm believer in the status quo, which in this case was his family.

*

Shortly thereafter, Ossie met Valerie, a virginal white girl from Minneapolis who was down on spring break, and they moved in together. A year later, they were married in a celebration the likes of which the island had never seen.

There was a parade, starring the black-suited, top-hatted YMCA marching band, with Ossie and his bride-to-be riding high atop an elaborate, dolphin-decorated float, and endless parties. On the evening following the formal

Anglican ceremony, in which Captain Brown served as best man and Warner was an usher, free liquor flowed at all the Brown establishments, and a good time was had by all.

Things changed after that. The free drinks and open bar tabs ceased; the Hemingway connection was played to the hilt with numerous photos and excerpts from his writing; and Ossie became the businessman his father had been before him.

Ossie and Warner's relationship changed, too. Valerie considered Warner part of the old days and the old ways that Ossie needed to leave behind if he were to assume leadership, and the evenings alone drinking gin ended unless Valerie happened to be in the States shopping or visiting her folks. Even then, the conversation was less animated, more formal and forced. It was as if Ossie had accepted the mantle of successorship, but along with power came regal responsibility and a necessary distancing of himself from his subjects.

Ossie and Valerie began to court the more staid and established of the boat crowd, and Valerie adopted a Bahamian accent thicker than any Biminite's.

Leader of the New Year's Day Parade

As the years passed, Ossie grew more and more distant. When he made the rounds of the bars, he was surrounded by an entourage of bartenders. His smiling, cocoa-colored visage graced worldwide ads for the Bahamas. He was photographed playing the congas and singing with the Calypsonians. Or sitting down to a friendly game of backgammon with an attractive white couple in the gleaming wood bar.

And yet . . .

There was a wistful sadness about Ossie. As his family grew—three daughters, one son —he became increasingly isolated. Apparent friend to all, but no one *his* friend.

*

Then came the break with Valerie. From the beginning, it was only a matter of time before she tired of island life. For an American, the days were monotonously one like another and the inconvenience—lack of shopping, no decent doctor or dentist or even plumber or mechanic, and the same old faces day in, day out—wore on one's nerves. Finally, Valerie had enough and moved her family, without Ossie, to Miami.

At first, Ossie (who, like his father before him, had acquired an island mistress) was relieved to see her go. But after awhile, he began to miss the children.

Ossie was thus adrift when Warner and he talked for the last time.

One night, after the bar closed, Ossie invited Warner back to his house to share a bottle of Tangueray. They took the bottle, limes, and tonic out on the front porch and pulled up chairs beside one another. It was a fine fall evening, with the wind blowing in from the Gulf Stream.

"Damn, I love it here, sometimes!" Warner exclaimed.

Ossie smiled his rueful smile. "Only sometimes?"

"You know what I mean. It's great for a while. But . . ."

Ossie finished his sentence. "You wouldn't want to live here." Then, following a long, pregnant pause, "Valerie feels the same way."

There was no rancor in Ossie's voice, only resignation. If he had to be a king without a queen, so be it. After all, maintaining Bimini's image was *his* job, not hers. She was just another seaweed who had washed ashore for a while, then drifted off.

As for his subjects . . .

Like most kings, Ossie was alternatively revered and despised. The Browns, especially Captain Brown, hadn't spent over half a century creating and maintaining their empire without arousing rancor and jealousy.

"I know. . . ." said Warner.

And for a moment, it was like old times.

*

Things happened quickly after that. A month later, Ossie was dead. Then Neville died of alcohol poisoning, and Spence drowned after his ship went down in a nor'easter. Captain Brown took to his bed with grief and was dead within the year, and Julian, the black sheep, was left in charge of the family empire.

Warner continued to visit. But with Ossie gone, something was missing.

The crown prince was dead, and for Warner, at least, Bimini would never be the same.

Picolo

≈

Picolo Pete was entering his ninety-fifth year, and he awoke early these days. The sun had just begun to light the pale pink horizon above Porgy Bay, when he edged his way carefully down the rickety wood staircase to the King's Highway. He paused at the downstairs entrance to the formidable concrete block building and gazed up lovingly at the red-lettered sign above the splintered door: "Precious de Paris Club."

The club belonged to Picolo. By night, he sang and played the banjo and served gut-wrenching home-brew to the few Biminites and seaweeds who drifted in; by day, he cut (or tried to cut) shady business deals.

In his day, Picolo had been (besides an entertainer) a fisherman, a smuggler, and a convict for killing a man in an argument over a card game. During the '30s, he skippered for Hemingway. He even wrote a song that appears in Papa's Bimini book, *Islands in the Stream*, and another, "Big Fat Slob in de Harbor," about a drunken brawl between Papa and a wealthy industrialist named Knapp over a record marlin. As far as your average Biminite is concerned, Papa's just another in a long line of drunken American fishermen. Picolo's the real folk hero—a man who once sold a gullible seaweed a South Bimini lot that was submerged at high tide.

Picolo took a padlock key out of the pocket of his chartreuse, bell-bottom trousers and unchained his rusty bike. He mounted the torn and taped seat and pedaled south on the Queen's Highway with a slow, wobbly-wheeled roll that defied gravity, on the lookout for beer cans to decorate his club's ceiling.

The night before had been even slower than usual, and Picolo wouldn't have had enough for grits 'n' grunts if his schoolteacher nephew, Ashley, hadn't bought a plastic baggie of grass. Bimini's drug traffic was pretty much a thing of the past since the U.S. Coast Guard had built a station on nearby Lighthouse Key. But small-time dealers like Picolo kept the locals supplied.

Neville's truck, with Accident riding in back with the garbage cans, passed with a grinding of gears, and Picolo pulled over to the side of the road to rest. Balancing the bike with his right foot, he took a worn white handkerchief out of his dusty trousers and mopped his shiny, jet-black forehead with it.

It was going to be a hot, wet day, he thought, another in a long line of hot, wet days since his birth.

Picolo wondered where the years—one seemingly like another, except for his brief incarceration at Foxhill in Nassau—had fled. His primary goal in life was turning a dollar to his advantage, yet here he was an old, old man, practically penniless. Had he been a philosopher, he might have wondered, "What's the use?" But he was no philosopher and faced each morning in the eager anticipation that today would be the day he'd make his fortune.

Up ahead, Picolo spotted a Conchy Joe striding out of the Angler's wood-gated stone entrance. As quickly as he could, Picolo pushed himself up on his bike and pedaled toward him.

The Conchy Joe, David Warner, was a writer from Florida, and Picolo had known him for nearly thirty years. Two or three years earlier, he would've recognized him, but not now. Age had softened his memory until Conchy Joes of years past faded into one another in a long, gray lineup. For him, the white-bearded Warner was Papa Hemingway.

Between '35 and '37, Hemingway made several voyages from Key West to Bimini aboard his sports fishing boat, the *Pilar*. He wrote parts of *To Have and Have Not* and *For*

Picolo Pete

Whom the Bell Tolls during the two or so months he spent there, and made a standing offer of $100 to anyone who could last three rounds in the boxing ring with him. Several tried; none succeeded.

"Papa, wait up!" shouted Picolo.

Warner stopped dead in his tracks. He turned and watched Picolo pedal up beside him.

"Going fishing for marlin dis morning?" asked Picolo. He held out his calloused hand. "Unloose a dollar, and I'll fetch back a mess of baits."

Warner knew all about Picolo and Hemingway's history. Picolo even claimed to have told Papa the story behind *The Old Man and the Sea*—"Papa just typed it up for me."

Following a whim, Warner decided to play along with Picolo's delusion and assume Hemingway's identity.

"I've got plenty of baits. What I need is a good first mate. Mine's in jail."

Picolo's face lit up like a jack-o-lantern. "I'm your man, Papa. I know de Gulf Stream like the back of my hand."

"All right, Pic. Meet me over at Brown's Dock in half an hour, and we'll cast off."

Picolo pedaled happily down the Queen's Highway, visions of a giant marlin and a corresponding tip dancing in his head.

*

Thirty minutes later, Picolo was waiting at Brown's when Warner arrived.

"I been waiting on you, Papa. Where's the *Pilar*?"

Warner attempted a diversion. "Little rough for fishing, don't you think?"

But Picolo knew better. Papa wanted to sit on the dock and listen to him spin yarns. He'd type them up later and sell them for a fortune.

Picolo smiled to himself. This time around, Papa wasn't going to get away with it.

"My yarns are worth money, Mr. Papa. A lot of it!"

Warner sighed. "I don't pay money for stories, Picolo. I make 'em up out of what I see and hear around me."

"Well, you won't be hearing any of mine!"

Picolo climbed abruptly back on his bike and pedaled north up the King's Highway, still on the lookout for beer cans.

Papa'll come around, he thought. And if he doesn't, Ashley can type just as good as him—maybe better. And he'll type for free so long as I supply him with dope. That way, the money I make will be all mine!

Bimini Y2K

≈

The West Indian is not exactly hostile to change, but he is not inclined to
believe in it. This comes from a . . . wisdom that his climate of eternal sum-
mer teaches him . . . [u]nder all the parade of human effort and noise, today
is like yesterday, and tomorrow will be like today . . . existence is a wheel of
recurring patterns from which no one escapes . . . the idea is to take things easy
and enjoy the passing time under the sun. The white people charging hopeful-
ly around the islands . . . making deals, bulldozing airstrips, hammering up
hotels . . . are to him merely a passing plague. They have come and gone
before.

— Herman Wouk, *Don't Stop the Carnival*

I t's January 4, Wednesday evening, in the year of Our
Lord 2000, and I'm addressing a conference of 150
Hemingway scholars on Bimini. Five evenings earlier

at midnight, during the dawning moments of the new millennium, I was seated on a bench looking out over the moonlit Gulf Stream at the shimmering glow of Miami, fifty nautical miles to the west, when a stranger appeared out of nowhere with a champagne bottle, and we silently toasted the next thousand years.

My friends Ossie, Coconut, and Accident are dead now, victims of time and drugs, but the island has changed little. That ancient patriarch of con men, Picolo Pete, is still selling South Bimini lots—that mysteriously vanish at high tide—to gullible seaweeds, and life goes on. . . .

Islands and I have a long history together. In a futile attempt to heal my troubled, teenage skin with sun and salt water, my parents and I covered the Caribbean and South Pacific on my school breaks, and I lost my virginity to a Trinidadian whore. When I came of age, I moved to Florida with its myriad of islands. The island lifestyle—unhurried, unworried, *mañana* takes care of itself—was something I admired and vainly tried to emulate.

As for Bimini, I first came here thirty years ago—fresh from reading the "Bimini" section of Hemingway's posthumously published novel in *Esquire*. Since that

Boat Captain with Ernest Hemingway

time, Bimini has become my lodestone, a measure of my deepest soul. With its *laissez-faire* outlook and natives who, as my friend Ashley Saunders puts it, "are always waiting for something to drop out of the sky or float up on the beach," Bimini remains a troublesome flea of drugs and smuggling on the dog of America, but *you* change. How is reflected in the way you view the island, which can be heaven or hell depending on the mood of the moment. As mystic-writer Emmett Fox writes in *The Sermon on the Mount*, "change in the outer picture becomes the visible evidence of . . . change in the inner—'an outward and visible sign of an inward and spiritual grace'—and thus we come to know unerringly where we stand. The outer picture is like the gauge that tells what is happening inside the boiler."

So I find myself on Bimini for the umpteenth time, reading an article I wrote about Papa's eccentric younger brother, Leicester, to a gathering of Hemingway scholars. Ironically enough, I met Les there twenty years before. If life's a cycle, I was coming full circle. But I was no longer the person I'd been twenty, or even ten, years before. Still, enough of the cynical residue of my former self was left over to make me uncomfortable. I, like my friend and literary mentor, the deceased southern novelist Borden Deal, didn't like or trust most college professors. I considered them rigid, humorless, petty, vindictive, and set in rationalistic ways that are the antithesis of creativity. To me, they were like the Pharisees of Jesus' time, well versed in law but ignorant of spirit. To again quote Fox: "Why was not the Christ message received with acclaim by the Ecclesiastics of Jerusalem? Because they had great possessions—possessions of Rabbinical learning, possessions of public honor and importance, authoritative office as the official teachers of religion—and those possessions they would have had to sacrifice . . . to accept the spiritual teaching. The humble and unlearned folk who heard the Master . . . were happy in having no such possessions to tempt them away from the Truth."

Earlier in the week, I'd observed the contrast between Biminites and academics. I was seated on the patio of the Compleat Angler when a couple of pasty-white intellectuals wafted over and put up a poster for the Ninth Annual Hemingway Conference, with dates and times, on the wood overhang facing the Queen's Highway. They'd no sooner departed than a disinterested Devil, the Angler's Biminite manager, stepped outside. Spotting the poster, he reached up and calmly ripped it free. Crushing it into a paper ball, he jump-shotted it into a nearby trash barrel. A Los Angeles Lakers fan *in extremis*. So much for organization!

Later, I listened to a couple of academic papers being read in the lumber-buttressed, freshly white-washed 1858 Wesley Methodist Church before escaping to the beach to snorkel. Hemingway's writing was being rationalized, symbolized, and psychoanalyzed to death. According to one professor, Hemingway lived on and wrote about islands—Key West, Cuba, Bimini—because he and his characters were isolated egotists. "I-Land." Get it? The academics were missing the point. What Hemingway wrote about so well in his island novels—fishing, drinking, socializing with the islanders—was overlooked while they listened to a lot of boring papers that might as well have been read in the Toledo, Ohio, Holiday Inn! A ten-hour seminar on bar-hopping would've better served Hemingway's spirit.

Meanwhile, Biminites were doing the same things they've always done—lazing about, arguing, fishing, conching, drinking, smoking dope, fucking, waiting for the big score to come down so they can make their fortunes—starting with the Carib Indians and later pirates, wreckers, and smugglers who used the island as a base of operations. But the Hemingway experts weren't paying any attention. They were too wrapped up in symbolism to notice reality.

So the conference progressed along its weary way. Derek Walcott, the Nobel Prize-winning Trinidadian poet, was flown in at a dead Papa's expense to address the gathering for a $15,000 fee. Mary Hemingway, Papa's widow, left all of his U.S. royalties to the Hemingway Society. Papa must've turned over in his grave!

But maybe I was missing the point by being spiritually arrogant, the deadliest of sins. In their dry, academic fashion, these people were enthusiasts, after all. Who was I to judge them? I read Hemingway because I enjoyed reading Hemingway. To them, he was a kind of religion. The God of Tenure.

I decided, Hemingway fashion, to get drunk and ponder the situation.

The End of the World Saloon—sand floor, rough-hewn walls festooned with magic-markered names and dates, hanging bras and panties, and a beautiful view of the blue-green harbor on the south end of North Bimini, near where Chalk's seaplanes (continuous service out of Miami since 1919 without a fatality) roar up on the con-

crete landing—is the perfect place for an afternoon libation. Adam Clayton Powell drank scotch and milk and
played dominoes here while network newsmen from the
States badgered him with questions. If it was good
enough for Adam, it was good enough for me.

The girl behind the graffiti-covered bar was cutting
and dicing conch, celery, and onions for conch salad,
and I bought a cup to eat with a cold, sweating bottle of
Kalik. Four intent, male Biminites were playing "killer"
dominoes at a rickety wood table off to the side, slamming the dominoes down so hard the tiny building shook.
Bang, bang, bang! Like gunfire. Everyone was smiling or
arguing or both, and I felt at home.

This is *my* Bimini. Not the Bimini of big game fishermen with multimillion-dollar boats and constant one-
upmanship over the biggest fish caught. Not even the
breathtakingly beautiful underwater world of the divers.
My Bimini is the people themselves with their easy
enjoyment of life, their acceptance of all that is pleasur-
able and blatant disregard for the rest. Campaigns and
causes, family and home life are not their forte. It's an
island of loners—or egoists, to substitute the negative
connotation of the academics—who enjoy the simple

things of life—food, drink, sex, and companionship. If materialism means the amassing of possessions, they aren't materialists. Any possessions they have are squandered with an unerring efficiency that would do a time-and-motion statistician proud. But they live with a life-affirming gusto that puts us Americans to shame!

I was musing thus when an academic walked up and peered cautiously inside. In a matter of moments, having analyzed the locals as a lepidopterist pins a butterfly (or so he thought), he was gone.

Why can't they enjoy themselves, I wondered. Stop their intellectualizing long enough to become living, breathing beings.

It was a question with no ready answer. Perhaps western civilization has advanced the intellect to the point where it's a burden rather than an asset. A crutch to steady us, while intuition—the still, small voice—atrophies. With the coming of the computer, the worldwide internet, about a million TV channels, and the cell phone, there's a glut of information. Information has become a sedative to drug us into a state of moral unconsciousness before the day is fairly begun. The

Roman Empire's "bread and circuses" with no moral center.

Biminites don't play that game. Rather, they accept the entertaining elements—pro sports, popular music—and ignore the rest. Their basic nature changed little during the twentieth century. They chose to sacrifice technology—air conditioners that always work, hard-spray showers, easily accessible long-distance phone calls, insurance, computers, and DUIs—for an attitude that accepts the individual on his own terms, regardless of so-called merits or demerits.

Still, life without modern conveniences in return for a more natural and intuitive lifestyle is a sacrifice most Americans wouldn't make. Is there a workable compromise? One involving both intuition and intellect, the right and left brain? One that would combine the Biminites' love of life and "live and let live" philosophy with modern conveniences and access to knowledge? I wondered. . . .

I'd spent the night before trying to sleep in a second-floor room at the Angler, while the Calypsonians, a Bimini band, pounded out the island beat:

Lay low on Bimini

Ain't nothing new

I been to Bimini before . . .

Eventually, the steadiness of the beat and the familiarity of the lyrics lulled me to sleep like mother's milk. Was I becoming a Biminite?

After falling asleep to the Calypsonians, I awoke in the middle of the night and wrote "Biminized" in my notebook, thinking I'd coined a new term.

The next morning, the rented skiff taking two friends and me snorkeling refused to start (the starter rope had somehow become hopelessly tangled), and we were attacked by relentless swarms of South Bimini no-see-ums. Eventually, an American mechanic came to our rescue. "I've never seen anything like this happen before!" he exclaimed with a shake of his graying head. "This boat has been *Biminized*!"

Apparently, the mechanic and I were on the same wavelength!

Bimini's relaxed and accepting atmosphere is conducive to psychic phenomenon. Later, I was introduced by Devil to Gregory Hemingway, Papa's youngest son.

"The other Hemingway," Devil called him. That was the title of the article I was to read before the Hemingway group later that evening!

I'm a writer, not a speaker. But, as I stood in the Methodist Church reading, I felt a sudden power welling within, the power of communication provided every man (if he reaches deep enough into heart and soul) by a beneficent God.

"On September 13, 1982, at approximately 2 P.M., Les Hemingway put the barrel of a .38-caliber Smith & Wesson revolver to his temple and fired off a round. His wife found him sprawled in the foyer, naked except for a pair of beige shorts. There was no note.

Bonefish Willie remembers Les as a man who was 'always reaching for something great . . . [but] he never quite grasped it.' "

The reading went well. At least, no one walked out, and the laughs came mostly in the right places. When I was done, though my piece hadn't been entirely complimentary to his uncle, one of Les's nephews came up to say how much he had enjoyed it. So, for a few moments at least, I reached out to what I considered an alien group, and we bonded.

On the last morning of the conference, a Sunday, everything was back to normal. At Capt. Bob's restaurant, a female academic took a prescription pill for her nerves and downed endless cups of coffee while perusing a week-old *New York Times*. At the same instant, Julian, a former drug smuggler and member of Bimini's first family, in burgundy choir robes that billowed in the breeze, took a hurried leak behind the pale white Anglican church, gazing down serenely at the bone-white beach and the pale blue Gulf Stream beyond.

Ashley

≈

Ashley awoke with a sense of renewed purpose. Recently, he'd composed a new poem, "Crazy Mon," and this afternoon he was going to present it to singer Jimmy Buffet as the proposed lyrics for a song. Jimmy was holed up on the south island writing a book, and Ashley knew him from way back when he used to perform at the Angler.

Rolling out of bed, Ashley lit a doobie and sucked in deep with a harsh, hissing sound. Then he dressed in long pants, white shirt, and dark tie for his daily stint as a schoolteacher. Just thinking about his unruly class made him feel weak. But that would soon be over. "Crazy Mon"

Ashley Saunders

was just the start. The world was crying out for an island songwriter, and he wasn't about to let them down.

Ashley lifted his briefcase, opened the door, and stepped outside. A cool breeze blew in from the sea, and the sun was a hazy, red ball over blue-green Porgy Bay. He walked briskly down the narrow, cluttered alleyway and turned north on the King's Highway. He nodded at Accident, who was hurriedly pushing his empty luggage cart in the opposite direction toward Chalk's; Coconut, barefoot, with trouser cuffs halfway up muscular brown calves, walked by, grinning idiotically.

The dive boat, with a fresh contingent of wide-eyed New Agers, was preparing to chug out to the Bimini Road, and Ashley walked over to confer briefly with Rick.

Ashley was almost to the barracks-like school when he realized how good it felt just being alive. Then, he recalled his unruly class and stepped behind a crooked palm to finish off his doobie.

One final toke, and all was right with the world. . . .

Bimini By The Sea, narrated by David Ogden Stiers, is now available on DVD and features forty-two minutes of island music, narration, and interviews about Bimini's colorful history, which has included rumrunners, drug smugglers, and such notable characters as writer Ernest Hemingway, exiled Harlem congressman Adam Clayton Powell, Jr., democratic presidential hopeful Gary Hart, and world-renowned psychic Edgar Cayce. Cayce predicted that the first remnants of the lost continent of Atlantis would be found off Bimini's shores—a prediction many explorers believe has come true. "More than a specific place, Bimini is a state of mind. . . ."

Ordering Information

DVD: $19.95 per copy
Call for shipping and handling information
334-265-6753
or toll free 877-408-7078

Mail check or money order (including $19.95 per copy and shipping costs as determined) to

Bimini By the Sea
River City Publishing
1719 Mulberry St.
Montgomery, AL 36106

For credit card orders call
334-265-6753
or toll free 877-408-7078